Janay,

Dream big and always remember

"You're Future is Bright!"

~ J.B. ~ 2/15/2021

MW00826539

College Girl's First

COLLEGE TOUR

JESSICA BROWN

Illustrated by **FELICIA WHALEY**

Jordan,
Dream big and always remember
"Your Future is Bright!"
#blessed
2/25/2021

College Girl's First College Tour

Published by College Gurl Publishing

P.O. Box 43783

Washington, D.C. 20010

Copyright © 2021 by Jessica L. Brown

All rights reserved. No part of this book may be reproduced, stored in a retrieval system, or transmitted in any form or by any means without the written permission of the publisher.

Illustrations by Felicia Whaley

ISBN-13: 978-0-578-80992-2

Library of Congress Control Number: 2020925635

DISCLAIMER AND/OR LEGAL NOTICES

While the publisher and author have used their best efforts in preparing this book, they make no representations or warranties with respect to the accuracy or completeness of the contents of this book. The advice and strategies contained herein may not be suitable for your situation. You should consult a professional where appropriate. Neither the publisher nor the author shall be liable for any loss of profit or any other commercial damages, including but not limited to special, incidental, consequential, or other damages. The purchaser or reader of this publication assumes responsibility for the use of these materials and information. Adherence to all applicable laws and regulations, both advertising and all other aspects of doing business in the United States or any other jurisdiction, is the sole responsibility of the purchaser or reader.

To The College Gurl Foundation. Continue to reveal
post-high school educational opportunities to youth,
and financing opportunities to parents,
so all children can know their future is bright.

—J.B.

Every weekday, Jessica wakes up before her alarm clock to get ready for school. She eats her breakfast and then rushes out to catch the school bus.

She sits in one of the first rows of the bus with her friends. Sometimes they talk, while other times Jessica listens to music and reads on the way to school.

Her language arts teacher, Mrs. Cook, often talks about college to prepare students for the future. One day, Mrs. Cook tells the class about an opportunity to attend a Historically Black College and University (HBCU) tour to visit the campus of Otis College in Washington, DC

She explains that a *campus* is the land and the buildings that make up a college or university.

Mrs. Cook says, "Students, check out this amazing opportunity to experience what college is like. You'll be able to experience college life, interact with college students, and explore the historical buildings on campus.
A bus will take students to visit Otis College.

"The tour will take place next week, and it's free!
I will be one of the chaperones on the trip. If you are interested, give this flyer to your parents so they can sign you up to attend the tour."

After Mrs. Cook's class, Jessica goes to lunch and shares the flyer with her friends. Jessica's best friend, Jasmine, says, "This is so cool! We will be the youngest kids on campus! We must go!"

Stephan and Lee fist bump and say, "It's lit!" while Alison and Kassidy read the tour schedule.

Jasmine wants to be a doctor. Stephan wants to be a musician. Alison wants to be an actress. And Jessica wants to be a news reporter. Jessica and her friends are so excited that they can't wait for school to let out.

At three o'clock school lets out, and Jessica cannot wait to get home to talk about the college tour with her mom.

At home, Jessica's mom reads the flyer. Right away, she signs up Jessica to go on tour.

Her mom says, "This is a tremendous opportunity to learn more about college with your friends, and it's never too early to begin thinking about it."

A couple of days later, her mom receives an acceptance letter for Jessica to attend the tour. Jessica jumps for joy and immediately starts calling friends to see if they have been accepted.

Sure enough, they are going too!

The night before the tour, she stares out the window, thinking about what college life will be like, college students, and things she will explore.

She has never visited a college campus before. She's so excited to experience it all that she can hardly sleep.

At five o'clock the next morning, Jessica is the first one to wake up and get dressed. One hour later, Jessica's mom drops her off at school to attend the tour.

Mrs. Cook does roll call and explains the schedule, events, and rules. As the bus begins to pull away, Jessica and her friends wave excitedly out the windows to their parents.

Since it was so early when the students boarded the bus, they all fall asleep during the drive.

When they wake up, the bus is parking at the illustrious Otis College in Washington, D.C.

As soon as Jessica sets foot on campus, the day becomes a whirlwind! She sees beauty, people, culture, and life that she has never seen before. Amazed by everything, she begins thinking about her future.

During the campus tour, the students can't stop raising their hands to ask questions of Tammy, the campus tour guide.

Jessica asks Tammy, "Is college free?"

Tammy answers, "If you earn good grades and scholarships, it can be. So it's really important to listen to your teachers and do your homework!"

Stephan asks, "What is a scholarship?" Tammy replies, "A scholarship is financial aid, which is free money awarded to outstanding students to help them pay for college."

Alison says, "I want to be an actress. Is there a theatre?"

All the students start talking about what they want to be.

Then Kassidy asks, "What is the point of college?"

Tammy explains, "A college education helps you learn the skills you'll need to get the job and the income you want."

She adds, "Anyone, from anywhere, can attend college."

The students follow Tammy as she guides them around the campus.

They visit the theatre,

television studio,

chemistry lab,

and dormitories.

Students are fascinated how incredible the classrooms are.

They even get to talk to college students!

Tammy also tells students about all the academic programs they offer and what Jessica and her classmates would be able to study in the future at the campus.

As the tour comes to an end, Tammy gives each of the visiting students a gift bag of college souvenirs and a journal.

Mrs. Cook does roll call, and the students board the bus to go back home.

As they drive home, Mrs. Cook gives the students an assignment. They are to write about things they saw and experienced on the trip. They'll share their stories the next day in class after they return home.

After the trip, the bus arrives back at school. Jessica's dad is there to pick her up. He looks happy that Jessica had this experience. He never went to college, but he has often talked about the importance of being a college graduate.

Jessica's father asks, "How was the tour?"

Jessica talks the whole way home. She can't wait to tell her mom about everything she got to see.

Her dad drops her off at their house. As he leaves for work, he says, "See you later, College Girl!"

Jessica Brown is a nationally recognized financial-aid expert. As founder of College Gurl, president of The College Gurl Foundation, and author of *How to Pay for College When You're Broke* and the children's book *College Girl's First College Tour*, Jessica educates students and families on how to make the best-informed decisions around financing a college education.

Named the Financial Aid Fairy Godmother, her mission is to ensure all students have access to affordable and quality education. Additionally, she mentors and exposes Washington metropolitan area high school students to college through her nonprofit, The College Gurl Foundation.

Jessica is a graduate of Howard University, Strayer University, and is currently seeking her PhD in higher education administration. She speaks all over the United States at a host of schools, universities, organizations, and news networks. Her work has been sponsored by Diversity Inc., Strayer University, and The Steve & Marjorie Harvey Foundation. She has recently been featured on the Tamron Hall Show, BET News, FOX Business Network, Essence Magazine, and several other news outlets.

Her philanthropic efforts have awarded her:

2020 HBCU Buzz's Top 30 Under 30

2020 WHUR 96.3 and McDonald's DMV Black Excellence Award

2019 Odyssey International's Outstanding Community Service Award of Excellence

2018 Dream 4 It Foundation's Dreamer Award

2018 Iota Phi Lambda Sorority, Inc.'s Power of She Award

Jessica makes her home in Washington, DC.

Teachers' Guide / Student Activites

DISCUSSION QUESTIONS:

1. What does each of you think you would like to be in your future career?

Answers will vary. Discussion ideas:

— Before the first student replies, reveal that each student will have unique abilities unlike anyone else's, and that all abilities that every person possesses matter and can make a positive difference in their future area of specialty.

— As each student replies, pause and acknowledge the importance and excitement of the career field the student specifies, keeping the focus on that one student for the moment.

— Then point out to that student a few strengths they already possess related to the career field they named.

— If you have noticed that a student has gifting for a career field other than the career field the student mentioned, point out that you've noticed they also have abilities that might work well for them if they had an interest in ___ (the career field you noticed the student may be a good fit for).

— If possible, specify one or more college classes they might pursue in the future, related to the career field they named.

— After the discussion that follows, have students complete and save Dear Future Me. Suggest they read it again on their eighteenth birthday.

2. What is a college campus?

— A campus is the land and the buildings that make up a college or university.

3. What kinds of things can a college student do on campus?

— A college student can attend classes; eat their meals in the cafeteria; live in dorm rooms on campus, which are like mini apartments; join social groups; meet friends from around the world, and much more.

4. Colleges are bigger than high schools. Can anyone guess the differences between a college and a university?

— Colleges are usually smaller than universities.

— Many people have colleges in or near their hometowns, while universities are usually located in bigger cities.

— Students at colleges can earn two-year degrees, such as an associates degree and a bachelor's degree. Students at universities can earn four-year degrees, such as a master's degree and a doctorate degree. Oftentimes, the more advanced your degree, the higher your income after graduation.

— Attending a college is usually more affordable than attending a university.

5. Can anyone go to college?

— Yes. It's possible for anyone, anywhere to attend college.

6. What qualities do you want your college to have? For example, would you like it to be big or small? Would you like the college to be located in a large city, a medium sized city, or a small town? Where in the United States would you like the college to be—near the ocean, in the mountains, in the country, in a warm climate, or somewhere else? Would you like the college to be religious or secular?

Answers will vary.

7. What skills do you need to master before going to college?

Answers will vary.

8. How do good grades help me get into college?

— Good grades, better chances of getting into college and receiving scholarships.

9. What type of short-term goals can be set to prepare myself for college?

Answers will vary.

10. When you graduate high school, you get a diploma. When you graduate college, you get a degree. What do you think a degree is?

— A degree is an award that says the student has successfully finished a course of study.

11. Does it matter if my parents went to college?

— It's possible for anyone, anywhere to attend college, whether or not his or her parents went to college.

12. What is a Historically Black College or University (HBCU)?

— A Historically Black College or University is an institution of higher learning established before 1964 whose primary focus was and is to educate Black Americans.

— HBCUs educate students of all races and nationalities.

Create the Dream, Build the Dream: Make a Vision Board to Forecast Your Future!

• By using magazines, cut out images that relate to you and your dreams. Create a collage and share your vision board and why you used those images.

Research Colleges and Universities Near You

• Name:

• Location:

• Campus Size:

• Cost:

• Academic Programs that Interest You:

• Campus Activities:

• Institutional Scholarships Provided:

Print and distribute copies of *Dear Future Me* for students to fill in during class discussion.

Dear Future Me,

Hi! Today is ___July 8___ (date). I'm __9__ years old, and I'm in
___Going to 4___ grade. My two favorite subjects in school are ___Math and art___ and
___art___. I also like to do ___basketball___ and ___among as___.
My least favorite food is ___Carrot___, but I love to eat ___cheeseburger___!
Right now my favorite song is ___Apecella___. Is it still one of your favorites?

During the next year, I hope that I learn to ___do do division better___.
Within three years, I hope to be able to ___open a dog walking baisness___
In __5__ years I'll graduate high school. By then, I really want to be good at
___being a vet (vet)___.

Today in Mr./Mrs./Miss___Rafalowsti___'s class we are talking about
going on a college tour! For my future job, I'd like to be a ___vet___. I
already have abilities that would help me do well in that career. Those abilities are
___Math___ and ___Animal body Science___   science
College classes that may help me to excel at that job include ___Medical___
and ___Math___.

At college I would also love to ___Join a Math te___and ___be a top math person___
I'd love to go to a college in this state or part of the country: ___New Jersey___.
Why? Because ___M I wanne be in my home town___
It's possible for anyone, anywhere to attend college. It's also possible for anyone,
anywhere to become whatever they want to be.

Future Me, which colleges or universities would you like to attend? ___Rutgers___
_____(I look forward to seeing you there!)
My best advice to my Future Me is ___Always be goa !___. It's been
amazing to talk with you! I can't wait to see which career we get to enjoy!

Love,
___Jangg (young goa)___ (Me)

Activity: Word Search

Print and distribute copies of *College Life Word Search* for students to complete.

College Life Word Search

X	P	O	A	C	A	D	E	M	I	C	S	H	K	S
N	F	E	D	U	C	A	T	I	O	N	G	Q	J	T
C	W	I	G	W	G	D	M	G	T	R	R	X	S	U
L	G	E	N	C	Q	R	E	D	Z	R	A	F	S	D
A	I	X	C	A	Z	S	A	G	G	I	D	U	S	E
S	D	P	O	U	N	V	U	D	R	I	E	T	C	N
S	O	E	L	N	C	C	G	N	U	E	S	U	H	T
R	R	R	L	I	Z	P	I	X	D	A	E	R	O	K
O	M	I	E	V	B	E	A	A	B	R	T	E	L	W
O	I	E	G	E	Z	U	B	A	L	N	I	E	A	S
M	T	N	E	R	W	L	U	H	F	A	O	Z	R	T
K	O	C	Z	S	Z	Z	E	I	P	W	I	L	S	U
M	R	E	I	I	I	B	H	P	E	A	P	D	H	D
L	Y	M	Q	T	H	O	M	E	W	O	R	K	I	Y
G	O	S	S	Y	Z	S	I	T	S	T	H	Q	P	N

WORD BANK

Academics   Education   Grades   Student

Classroom   Experience   Graduate   Study

Degree   Financial Aid   Homework   University

Dormitory   Future   Scholarship

College Life Word Search Answer Key:

X	P	O	A	C	A	D	E	M	I	C	S	H	K	S
N	F	E	D	U	C	A	T	I	O	N	G	Q	J	T
C	W	I	G	W	G	D	M	G	T	R	R	X	S	U
L	G	E	N	C	Q	R	E	D	Z	R	A	F	S	D
A	I	X	C	A	Z	S	A	G	G	I	D	U	S	E
S	D	P	O	U	N	V	U	D	R	I	E	T	C	N
S	O	E	L	N	C	C	G	N	U	E	S	U	H	T
R	R	R	L	I	Z	P	I	X	D	A	E	R	O	K
O	M	I	E	V	B	E	A	A	B	R	T	E	L	W
O	I	E	G	E	Z	U	B	A	L	N	I	E	A	S
M	T	N	E	R	W	L	U	H	F	A	O	Z	R	T
K	O	C	Z	S	Z	Z	E	I	P	W	I	L	S	U
M	R	E	I	I	I	B	H	P	E	A	P	D	H	D
L	Y	M	Q	T	H	O	M	E	W	O	R	K	I	Y
G	O	S	S	Y	Z	S	I	T	S	T	H	Q	P	N

Made in the USA
Middletown, DE
16 February 2021

33890453R00022